Writing Li

Writing in all Curriculums

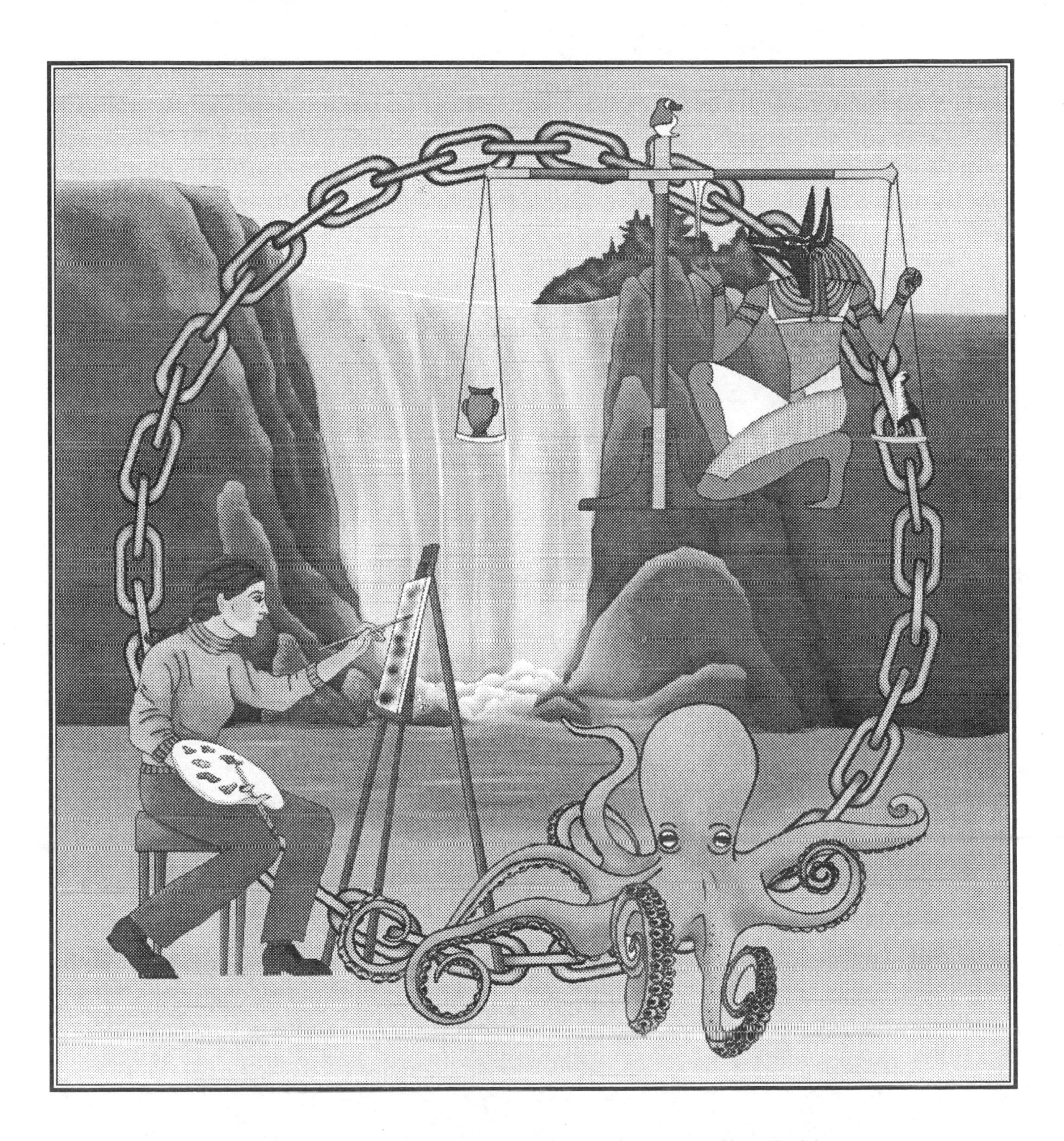

Written by Charlotte Jaffe and Barbara Doherty
Cover Illustrated by Koryn Agnello
Text Illustrated by Koryn Agnello & Karen Sigler

ISBN 1-56644-035-1

EDUCATIONAL IMPRESSIONS, INC.
Hawthorne, NJ 07507

Printed in the United States of America.

Table of Contents

Overview

Writing Links provides students with the much-needed opportunity to integrate and expand their writing skills in different areas of the curriculum. The four distinct themes in this book are Ancient Civilizations, The Sea, Creative People, and Natural Wonders. Each unit includes writing links in the following subject areas: Social Studies, Science, Math, Language, Poetry, Reading, Art, and Music. Thought-provoking writing projects inspire students to improve their techniques in expository writing, persuasive writing, narrative writing, evaluative writing, and creative writing. Students are given opportunities to write alone, with a partner, and with a small cooperative group.

Among the varied writing projects are the following activities: writing a letter, writing poetry, writing word problems, writing lyrics for a song, creating myths, writing a sports broadcast, writing a speech, and more. Because the activities in *Writing Links* are self-directed, you and your students will find this resource to be not only motivating and informative, but also easy to use.

ALSO INCLUDED IN THIS RESOURCE:

Writing Skills Checklist: The Writing Skills Checklist on the following page offers students a guide for improving their writing skills. The page should be duplicated for each student's use.

Optional Writing Activities: Optional Writing Activities are provided for each thematic unit.

Bibliography: A limited bibliography is provided at the end of the book.

Answers: Answers to a few math links are provided at the bottom of this page.

ANSWERS TO SELECT ACTIVITIES:

ROMAN NUMERALS (Page 12)
XXXVI = 36
CCLXXXVII = 287
400 = CD
90 = XC

MATH IN ANCIENT EGYPT (Page 13)

132 = 𓍢𓎆𓎆𓎆𓏺𓏺

1/4 = 𓂋𓏽

MEASURING THE SEA (Page 26)
ANSWER TO WORD PROBLEM: 66 feet

WRITING SKILLS CHECKLIST

The following are some guidelines to remember when you write.

WRITING GUIDELINES

___ 1. Did you compose a good opening sentence that will catch the attention of the reader?

___ 2. Do you have a single focus in your writing? Did you stick to one topic?

___ 3. Did you make sure that your writing is organized? Does it progress logically from beginning to end? Is it clearly written and easy to follow?

___ 4. Did you use details in your writing that clarify and support the main topic?

___ 5. Did you make sure that your writing is accurate? Did you check carefully for grammar, spelling, and punctuation errors?

___ 6. Did you write in a legible manner? Will people be able to read your work easily?

___ 7. Did you use vivid vocabulary in your writing? Are your words interesting and colorful?

___ 8. Did you use sentence variety in your writing? Are your sentences of varied lengths? Did you start your sentences with different words?

___ 9. Did you use word variety in your writing? Check to see that you did not use the same word over and over.

___ 10. Did you try the use of transitional sentences between paragraphs? They make your writing easier to follow and understand.

___ 11. Did you use a good closing sentence? Does it sum up your writing in an effective way?

___ 12. Did you check your first draft carefully before attempting to revise and rewrite your work?

Section I:

Ancient Civilizations

Ancient Architecture

When we think of ancient Egypt, ancient Greece, and ancient Rome, we picture famous structures that exemplify each civilization. The Great Pyramid and King Tut's tomb are associated with ancient Egypt. The Parthenon is one of the most beautiful temples built in ancient Greece. The Colosseum is a remnant of life in ancient Rome. There are many more examples of notable ancient architecture that still exist.

Research a famous structure from each of the ancient cultures mentioned above. Find out about the materials used to make them, their various functions, who designed and built them, and other significant information. Write these facts in the spaces below. Assemble them into an informative and cohesively written essay. Compare and contrast the structures. If possible, draw or locate a picture of each structure to add to your report.

FAMOUS STRUCTURES

ANCIENT EGYPT

Name of structure: ______________________________

Important facts: ______________________________

____

____

ANCIENT GREECE

Name of structure: ______________________________

Important facts: ______________________________

____

____

ANCIENT ROME

Name of structure: ______________________________

Important facts: ______________________________

____

____

A Gift to the Future

The ancient cultures of Egypt, Greece, and Rome developed new ideas that enriched the lives of the civilizations that followed. The ancient Egyptians developed *papyrus,* a type of paper made from a water plant. This invention enabled people to write down their ideas on scrolls and later in book form. The ancient Greeks gave us early ideas about a democratic form of government. The ancient Romans were skilled builders and engineers. The creation of the arch was one of their ideas.

Divide into three teams: Ancient Egypt, Ancient Greece, and Ancient Rome. Investigate other inventions handed down by these cultures. List them on the chart and explain their significance.

ANCIENT EGYPT

Name of invention: ______________________

Why significant: ____

Name of invention: ______________________

Why significant: ____

Name of invention: ______________________

Why significant: ____

ANCIENT GREECE

Name of invention: ______________________

Why significant: ____

Name of invention: ______________________

Why significant: ____

Name of invention: ______________________

Why significant: ____

ANCIENT ROME

Name of invention: ______________________

Why significant: ____

Name of invention: ______________________

Why significant: ____

Name of invention: ______________________

Why significant: ____

The Nile River Cycle

Long ago on the banks of the Nile River, the ancient Egyptians made markings on a large stone. These markings are thought to be measurement symbols for the Nile River's rise and fall. The Nile, the world's longest river, is 4,132 miles (6,648 km.) long.

Research the Nile River and its cycle. Why is this river so important to the Egyptian people? What are the consequences of the river's seasonal floods?

Write a short essay answering the following question: If you were a citizen of ancient Egypt and lived in the Nile River Valley, why would the cycle markings of the river be essential?

Constellations

The ancient Egyptians observed the stars and made astronomical drawings showing the constellations as gods. This and their studies of the flooding of the Nile River enabled them to invent a calendar of 365 days. The ancient Greeks and Romans also studied the sky and named groups of stars they viewed as their gods. Many of the constellations we observe today still bear the names of the ancient gods, heroes, and beasts. Many myths were written to explain the constellations.

THE CONSTELLATION OF ORION, THE HUNTER

Orion was a mighty hunter who fell in love with the goddess Artemis. Her brother Apollo did not like Orion and planned to kill him. Apollo tricked Artemis into shooting an arrow into her lover, thinking he was a target in the water. In sorrow, Artemis placed Orion in the sky as a constellation.

Learn how other constellations got their names. List them in the chart below.

NAME OF CONSTELLATION	ORIGIN OF NAME

Choose one constellation that does not have a tale describing it. Find out its location in the sky and make a sketch of it. Create a story behind the name. Write and illustrate your story on another sheet of paper.

Roman Numerals

The ancient Romans used capital letters to write numerals. Today, Roman numerals are still used on some clock and watch faces, for the display of dates, and for numbering outlines.

The Roman numerals and their equivalents in cardinal numbers (the numbers we use in counting and to show order) are shown below.

ROMAN NUMERAL	CARDINAL NUMBER
I	1
V	5
X	10
L	50
C	100
D	500
M	1,000

When one of the symbols I, X, or C precedes a Roman numeral of greater value, its value is subtracted from the greater value.

Examples: **IV** = 5 – 1 = 4 **IX** = 10 – 1 = 9 **XL** = 50 – 10 = 40 **CM** = 1,000 – 100 = 900

What cardinal number does each of the following Roman numerals express?

XXXVI: ___________ CCLXXXVII: ___________

Write a Roman numeral for each of the following cardinal numbers.

400: ___________ 90: ___________

Create your own Roman numeral word problems. Explain in writing how you arrived at the correct answers.

____

____

____

____

____

____

Math in Ancient Civilizations

Ancient Egyptians created picture symbols to write whole numbers and fractions. They used basic symbols for whole numbers.

Egyptian Symbol	𓏺	𓎆	𓍢	𓆼	𓂭
Value	1	10	100	1,000	10,000

How would the Egyptians have written the number 132? ____________________

The ancient people also had a way of representing fractional numbers. They used unit fractions with a numerator of one.

Egyptian Symbol	𓂋𓏻	𓂋𓎆	𓂋𓎆𓏻	𓂋𓍢	𓂋𓆼
Unit Fraction	1/2	1/10	1/12	1/100	1/1,000

Use Egyptian symbols to write the unit fraction for 1/4. ____________________

Evaluate the Egyptian number system. Write a paragraph to explain why this number system might be difficult to use.

Fashions of the Ancient World

Ancient Romans wore *togas,* loose one-piece garments. These articles of clothing were worn by draping them over the body in folds. At first, most togas were made of wool. Later, linen togas were also popular. Senators wore togas that had wide purple stripes on them.

The basic Greek fashion was called a *chiton,* which was a loose, flowing tunic. Chitons were made from pieces of linen or muslin. Women's chitons were longer and fuller than the men's.

Egyptian men and women wore elaborate jewelry made of gold, copper, silver, and various precious stones. Men wore garments shaped like loin cloths; these garments resembled aprons or skirts. Some were pleated. The women favored long, straight dresses with straps at the shoulders.

Pretend that you are a fashion commentator. Write a short script for an Ancient Civilization Fashion Show. Describe each model's apparel.

Speak Out

The ancient Greeks and Romans admired people who where skilled in public speaking. These people were called orators. Cicero was a famous orator who lived in ancient Rome from 104 to 43 B.C. He was noted for his fiery speeches in the Roman Senate.

Imagine that you are a member of the Roman Senate and prepare a speech that you will present to your peers. Before composing your speech, research some facts about the Roman government and learn the responsibilities of the members of the Senate. Talk about an issue that might be facing the citizens of the Roman Empire.

Write your speech in the space below. Highlight certain words to be emphasized when you read your speech aloud to your classmates.

Lyric Poetry

Lyric poetry is a popular form of poetry writing that was started by the ancient Greek poets. The word *lyric* comes from the word *lyre,* a stringed instrument that was used to accompany the the Greeks' poetry readings. Lyric poems were recited by one person or by a large group of people called a *chorus*. One form of lyric poetry is called an *ode*. An ode is a serious poem, usually written to honor or praise a person or a special object. Read the odes written by John Keats and William Wordsworth.

Write the first draft of your original poem in the space below. Then write your final copy on another sheet of paper. Decorate it and hang it on a bulletin board.

____
(Title)

Mythology

The people who lived in ancient times created myths to explain things that they did not understand: the changing seasons, the roar of thunder, echoes, the origin of the earth. Lessons in moral values were also taught in myths. In Greek mythology, Heracles helped society by ridding it of terrible monsters and evil people. Gods and goddesses often appeared in myths. Many gods possessed human qualities even though they were immortal and very powerful.

Read a myth from each of the following cultures: ancient Egypt, ancient Greece, and ancient Rome. Write the name of each myth in the space provided. In a few well-written sentences, summarize the main theme of the story.

ANCIENT EGYPT

Title of Myth: ______________________________

Summary of Myth ______________________________

____

____

____

ANCIENT GREECE

Title of Myth: ______________________________

Summary of Myth ______________________________

____

____

____

ANCIENT ROME

Title of Myth: ______________________________

Summary of Myth ______________________________

____

____

____

Choose one of the above myths and create a new ending for it. Share your creative project by reading your myth aloud to your classmates. Illustrate your myth.

The Egypt Game

By Zilpha Snyder

The Egypt Game is about two girls, Melanie Ross and April Hall, who share an interest in ancient Egypt. They decide to recreate the ancient land on an empty neighborhood lot and to call it the Egypt Game.

Read the book. Then answer the following questions in essay form.

1. In the story, April changes her feelings about her grandmother. Write a narrative essay about a time when your relationship with a friend or family member changed. Explain the reason for the change.

2. Describe the information you learned about ancient Egypt as a result of reading this book.

3. Describe one story problem and tell how you would have solved it differently.

Hieroglyphic Writing

From the writings and carvings of the ancient Egyptians, we have learned a great deal about what happened in their civilization. These people developed a rough paper from the papyrus plant on which they wrote accounts of what they did using hieroglyphic characters. A rock called the Rosetta Stone helped scientists decode the language and understand the meaning of the hieroglyphics. Carvings found on stone walls gave clues to life in ancient Egypt.

Here are some hieroglyphic characters used by the ancient people. Research other hieroglyphs and add them to those below. Use the characters to write an original story about life in ancient Egypt. Substitute the hieroglyphs for words as in a rebus story.

Making Music

Music was an important part of life in the ancient civilizations. The Egyptians played a variety of musical instruments, including drums, clarinets, harps, and lutes. People sang songs and danced to the music, especially at banquets or parties. Ancient Greeks played lyres and the *aulos,* an instrument similar to the oboe. The Greeks also composed and sang their own songs at festivals, banquets, and ceremonies. In ancient Rome, travelling musicians, called *joculators,* roamed the countryside playing different types of musical instruments.

Pretend that you are a citizen of one of the ancient lands described above. Compose lyrics for a song that describes a life situation. Add music and perform it for your classmates.

____

(Song Title)

____

____

____

____

____

____

____

____

____

____

____

____

____

____

Section II:

The Sea

Endangered Sea Life

Throughout the seas of our world, populations of certain fish and sea animals have declined. The reasons for this problem vary according to the particular species and habitat. In Florida's waters the manatees are at risk due to increased recreational boating; death or injury often results from collisions with boat propellers. Marine turtles sometimes suffer as a result of factory waste and oil spills. Many turtles choke on debris, balloons, plastic bags, and styrofoam pieces left in the water. Illegal harvesting of some species of fish also takes its toll.

Use your computer or school library reference materials to compile a list of endangered or threatened sea lie. Then compose a letter to:

Office of Protected Resources
National Marine Fisheries Service
315 East-West Highway, 13th Floor
Silver Spring, MD 20910

In your letter, ask what you, your family, and your friends can do to keep our sea life safe. Follow the correct letter writing form, and be sure to include a return address on the envelope.

Write the first draft of your letter in the space below.

Living by the Sea

Venice, Italy, a popular tourist destination, has streets of water that empty into the Adriatic Sea. The cities of Amsterdam and Rotterdam in the Netherlands are busy shipping centers because of their locations near the sea. In Japan, an island nation, fishing is a major industry. In many other parts of the world, the way of life is determined because of proximity to an important waterway. Can you name a few? Tell how these place are influenced by their nearness to the sea.

LOCATION	HOW INFLUENCED
______________________	____________________________
______________________	____________________________
______________________	____________________________
______________________	____________________________
______________________	____________________________
______________________	____________________________
______________________	____________________________

Choose one location that you have named. Create an advertising brochure about it. In the brochure, discuss the importance of the sea to the survival and prosperity of the citizens. Write your ideas for the advertising brochure in the space below.

Sea Categories Game

Identify the sea life that is pictured on this page. Research some facts about each. For example, learn about their appearance, their habitat, how they protect themselves, and their importance in nature. Then put the sea life into categories and give each category a name. You may put the same picture into more than one category. Write a short essay telling the reasons for selecting those categories.

A Zoo at Sea

Have you ever heard of a catfish, a dogfish, or a sea horse? These and other sea animals have the name of a land animal in their names. Divide your class into small cooperative-learning groups. Work together and see how many other names you can add to this list. After brainstorming time is over, compare your list with those of other groups. Use research materials to obtain information about the sea animals and locate illustrations of them. Create a class Sea Zoo by drawing pictures of the sea life and mounting them on heavy paper or cardboard.

Display the completed pictures on a table or bulletin board in your classroom. Summarize the information that you have researched about each sea creature and write the facts on cards. Place each card next to the proper sea animal.

OUR GROUP LIST

SEA ANIMAL	HABITAT	CHARACTERISTICS	SKETCH

Measuring the Sea

Special units of measure apply to the sea.

A **KNOT** is a unit of speed at sea. It is equal to one **NAUTICAL MILE** per hour.

A **NAUTICAL MILE** measures distance. It is equal to 6,076 feet (1,852 meters).

A **FATHOM** measures depth. It is equal to 6 feet (1.83 meters).

Suppose you spotted buried treasure on the ocean bottom and that it was 11 fathoms down, directly below you. How many feet would you have to swim to reach it?

SOLUTION:

Use the measurement information above to create three of your own word problems. Exchange them with a classmate to solve. (Be sure you know the correct solutions!)

1. ____

____

Answer ____________________________________

2. ____

____

Answer ____________________________________

3. ____

____

Answer ____________________________________

Sea Statistics

1. Flying squid can leap 20 feet out of the water and glide through the air for 60 yards. Imagine how they can scare sailors!
2. The largest known octopus washed up on a beach in Florida. It was 200 feet in width. The smallest octopus is only two inches in width.
3. Sea otters eat up to 20 pounds of food each day.

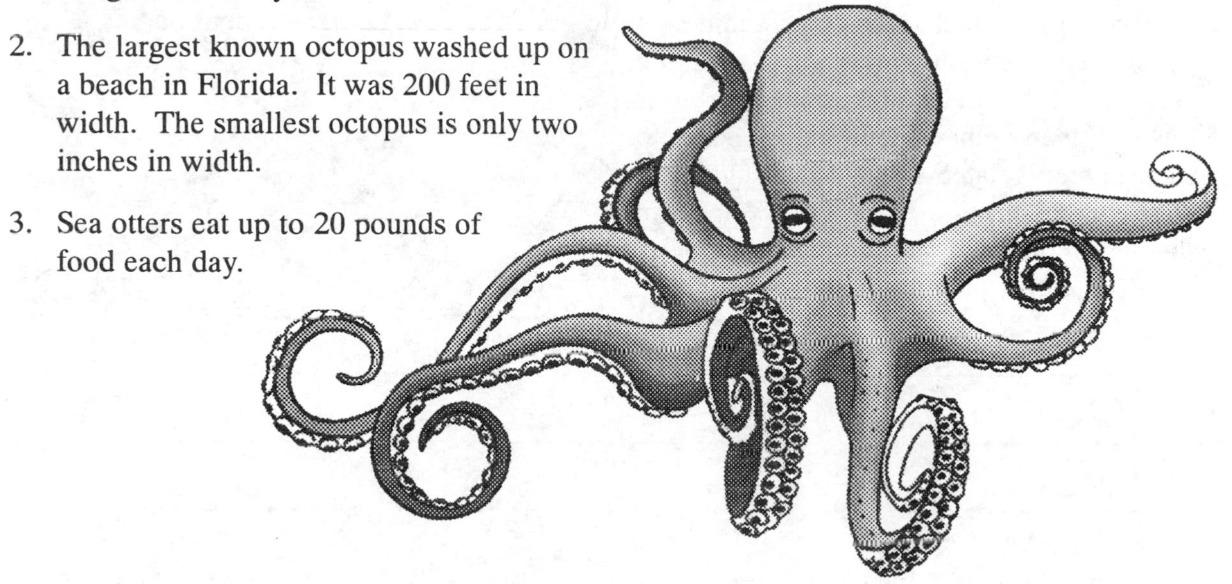

Locate other sea statistics and put them on a classroom chart. Use the information to compare and contrast life in the sea. Use the chart form below to record information.

Name of Sea Life	Size	Special Characteristics	Appearance	Habitat

Use the information on the chart to create three word problems. Exchange them with a classmate to solve.

Humans at Sea

Jacques-Yves Cousteau was a famous ocean explorer, author, and film maker. He invented new techniques and equipment that enabled people to explore the sea more efficiently. Although not as well known as Cousteau, many other people have chosen to pursue careers related to the sea. Fishermen, divers, and marine biologists perform valuable services. Can you think of any other occupations that fit this category?

____

____

____

Pretend that you have chosen a career at sea. Write a diary entry from the first-person point of view detailing a typical day in your life.

Date ____________________

Dear Diary,

____

____

____

____

____

____

____

____

____

____

Mythical Monsters

Over the years, people have reported sightings of unusual sea creatures. Scientists have explained many of these "scary sea monsters" away. A pair or a group of sea animals swimming close to each other, for example, may give the appearance of one long sea creature. Other "sea monsters" remain a mystery, however. Some people believe that the Loch Ness Monster, nicknamed Nessie, inhabits Loch Ness, a lake in northern Scotland. Although people claim to have photographs of this creature, scientific experts still cannot agree on what the photos actually show.

Use your imagination to create your own sea monster. Describe its appearance and habitat. What special characteristics does it have? Why is it fearsome? Give the monster a name, and use it as the main character in a creative story. Be sure to provide an illustration of it on another page.

Begin your story here:

Japanese Poetry

An ancient form of Japanese poetry is called a **haiku**. This verse has only three lines. The first and third lines have five syllables, and the second line has seven syllables. These poems usually have nature as a theme. Haikus do not have to rhyme.

Here is a sample haiku poem based on the book *The Big Wave,* written by Pearl Buck. It is about a tsunami that damages a village and the lives of its residents. (A tsunami is a very large wave caused by an underwater volcanic eruption or earthquake. It is sometimes called a tidal wave, although it has nothing to do with the tides.)

THE ANGRY WAVE

With its mighty force
The big wave destroyed our homes
Then quickly vanished.

Create two haikus that describe scenes from the sea. The poems could reflect an experience you have had or an observation you have made. Share your haikus orally with your classmates.

HAIKU # 1

HAIKU # 2

Call it Courage

By Armstrong Sperry

You will enjoy reading the story of Mafatu, an island boy who, although he feared the sea, had the courage to overcome his fright.

After you have completed the reading of the book, answer the following questions in essay form:

1. Be a critic. Pretend that you are a reporter for a local newspaper. Write a review of the book. Summarize the story and highlight important parts. Discuss the author's writing style and use of vocabulary. Evaluate the book and give reasons for your opinions.

2. Describe the information you learned about the sea as a result of reading this book.

3. What lesson did you learn from this book that you can apply to your own life?

The Big Wave

By Pearl S. Buck

The story of two young Japanese friends, Jiya and Kino, is an inspiring one to read. Jiya bravely endures a sudden family tragedy. He is able to conquer his fears and enjoy a full life.

After you have completed the reading of the book, answer the following questions in essay form:

1. If you were the Old Gentleman, how would you persuade Jiya to live with you instead of living with Kino's family?

2. Explain how Jiya's life has been changed by the big wave.

3. Discuss the information you learned about the sea as a result of reading this book.

Sea Paintings

The sea has often been a great source of inspiration for artists. Winslow Homer, J.M.W. Turner, and Paul Gauguin are three artists who painted scenes of the sea. Use reference books or the computer to locate a reproduction of a work of art by any of the three men.

Title Of Painting ______________________ Artist ______________________________

In a short paragraph, give your impression and opinion of the work of art. What is happening in the painting? How does the painting make you feel?

____

____

____

____

____

____

Learn more about these artists and their styles or painting. Write the information you learn in report form on another sheet of paper. Try to draw your own sea painting in the form of one or all of the artists. Sketch your drawing in the box below.

Create a Sea Chantey

A **chantey** (or shantey or shanty) is a song chanted by sailors in rhythm with their motion as they work on their boats. The crew members sing the melodies as they haul sails, adjust riggings, or attend to other on-board duties.

One famous sea chantey is "Blow the Man Down." It begins…

> "Come all ye young sailors who follow the sea,
> With a Yo Ho, blow the man down."

With your cooperative-learning group, create an original sea chantey. Perform it for your classmates. Write your lyrics in the space below.

Section III:

Creative People

Cleopatra

Cleopatra was a ruler of ancient Egypt. Lengend tells us that she gained favor with the conquering Romans by concealing herself in a carpet, which was then presented to Caesar as a gift. This would have been a creative way to create a good bargaining situation for herself and her country.

The following is one definition of creativity: "Characterized by originality and expressiveness; imaginative."* Research the following people. Cite an example that shows how each of these people showed his or her creativity.

Thomas Jefferson: ______________________________

____

Marion Anderson: ______________________________

____

Louis Daguerre: ______________________________

____

Pablo Casals: ______________________________

____

Emma Lazarus: ______________________________

____

Choose one of the above people. Write a paragraph in which you explain how this person showed creativity.

____

____

____

____

____

____

____

* *The American Heritage College Dictionary, Third Edition.* Boston: Houghton Mifflin, 1993.

Creativity throughout History

Creativity takes many forms and is not limited to any one part of our world. Neither has creativity been limited to any one period of history. Alexander Graham Bell, a Scotish-born American, invented the telephone in 1876. The Italian Leonardo da Vinci, who lived from 1452 to 1519, showed his creativity in many ways; he was a musician, a painter, an engineer, and a scientist. The great English playwright and poet William Shakespeare lived from 1564 to 1616. All of these people showed great creativity in their work.

Choose two of the people listed below. Write a paragraph about each. Provide details about where and when in history each lived, including his or her most creative period. For each, explain the form his or her creativity took. Then name the person's major works or inventions.

Homer	Louis Armstrong	Benjamin Franklin	Georgia O'Keeffe
Claude Monet	John Lennon	Beatrix Potter	Rembrandt van Rijn
Samuel F.B. Morse	Berta Hummel	Plácido Domingo	Ludwig von Beethoven

NAME: ______________________________

____

____

____

____

____

____

NAME: ______________________________

____

____

____

____

____

____

EXTRA: ***Make a Creativity Time Line!***
Choose a field of creativity; for example, art, music, the sciences, inventions, writing, or poetry. Create a time line that shows where and when in history creative people in this field lived.

Marie Curie

Marie was born in Warsaw, Poland, in 1867. Her parents were school teachers. She travelled to Paris, France, to study. It is there that she met and married Pierre Curie, a professor at the university where she studied. Together they conducted research about the radioactivity of certain substances. Marie accomplished a great deal during her lifetime. Learn more about Marie Curie's work, discoveries, honors, and accomplishments.

Write ten facts that you would include if you were to write a biography of Marie Curie. Be sure to write in complete sentences.

1. ______________________________

2. ______________________________

3. ______________________________

4. ______________________________

5. ______________________________

6. ______________________________

7. ______________________________

8. ______________________________

9. ______________________________

10. ______________________________

George Washington Carver

George Washington Carver was born a slave in the 1860s in Diamond Grove, Missouri. He grew up to be one of the most respected scientists in America. In 1896 Carver was asked by Booker T. Washington to come to Alabama and join his staff at the Tuskegee Institute, where an expert in agricultural science was needed. George Washington Carver, who had already become a renowned botanist, became that expert.

In 1920 Carver was asked to speak to the Ways and Means Committee of Congress on behalf of the United Peanut Association. The committee members were about to discuss a tariff on the plant, which they believed was virtually useless. Carver stunned them by telling them about the hundreds of uses for the peanut he and his researchers had found. By the end of the day, Carver had them all on his side.

George Washington Carver was a **botanist,** a scientist who specializes in the study of plants. Other kinds of scientists are listed in the box below. Look up the meaning of each. For each word, write a question for which each would be the answer. Try to vary your sentences. Three examples for "botanist" follow:

What type of scientist was George Washington Carver?
What type of scientist specializes in the study of plants?
What scientist would probably know the scientific name for a tulip?

chemist	physicist	zoologist	meteorologist	biologist	geologist

____

____

____

____

____

____

____

____

Putting a Price on Creativity

Some people pursue creative activities for the pure enjoyment of it. Many artists, authors, inventors, and other creative people, however, use their creativity to earn a living. Often it is difficult to put a price tag on that creativity.

Suppose that you are an artist about to show your paintings at a local art show. You know the following facts:

You had to make the following expenditures:

Paint: $35.00
Brushes: $55.00
Canvases: $36.00
Booth fee for art show: $75.00

You have ten paintings to show.

It took you a total of three hundred hours to complete all of the paintings.

Write two word problems based on the above information. You do not have to use all the facts in your problems and you may add other facts. Make sure that you know the correct solutions to your problems. Exchange problems with your classmates. Compare your solutions.

WORD PROBLEM #1:

____

____

____

____

SOLUTION:

WORD PROBLEM #2:

____

____

____

____

SOLUTION:

Royalty Word Problems

Authors and composers often receive royalties for their published works. A royalty is a share of the proceeds received from the sale or performance of a work.

Using the following facts about the royalties received by a particular author, create math word problems:

> The author wrote three books for a certain publisher.
>
> According to her contract, the author was to receive as a royalty 10% of the money received by the publisher from the sale of those books. The money was to be paid semi-annually.
>
> In a period of six months, the publisher received the following amounts from the sale of the author's books:
> Book No. 1: $2,500.00
> Book No. 2: $1,900.00
> Book No. 3: $1,200.00
>
> In the previous six-month period, the author received $650.00 in royalties from the same three books.

Write two word problems based on the above information. You do not have to use all the facts in your problems and you may add other facts. Make sure that you know the correct solutions to your problems. Exchange problems with your classmates. Compare your solutions.

WORD PROBLEM #1:

____

____

____

SOLUTION:

WORD PROBLEM #2:

____

____

____

SOLUTION:

And Then Walt Said. . .

Choose two of the creative individuals from the following list. Research each. Then write an imaginary dialogue that might take place if the two could meet. Remember to set the scene for the reader by providing the necessary background information on the individuals.

Thomas Edison	Walt Disney	Orville or Wilbur Wright	Maya Angelou
I.M. Pei	Wolfgang A. Mozart	Bruce Springsteen	Michelangelo
Mary Cassatt	Elias Howe	Diego Rivera	Galileo Galilei

DIALOG BETWEEN: ______________________ **and** ______________________

TOPIC TO BE DISCUSSED: ____

Write your dialogue on the lines below. Indicate each speaker.

_________________________: ________________________________

____

_________________________: ________________________________

____

_________________________: ________________________________

____

_________________________: ________________________________

____

_________________________: ________________________________

____

_________________________: ________________________________

____

_________________________: ________________________________

____

_________________________: ________________________________

____

_________________________: ________________________________

____

Creative Problem Solving

Many serious problems affect the world today. Some examples are pollution, lack of food and energy supplies, drugs, and terrorism. Try to think of other problems we face. Add as many as you can to the list.

Air Pollution
Water Pollution
Terrorism
Drugs

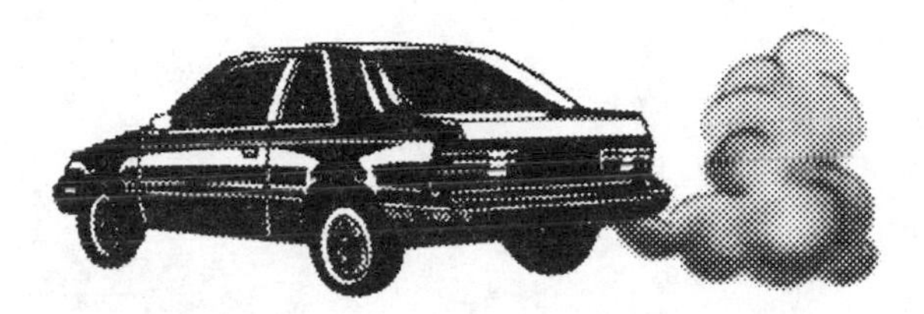

Now choose one of those problems. Think of a creative way to ease the problem.

THE PROBLEM:

____

____

____

CREATIVE SOLUTION:

____

____

____

____

____

Many inventions are created as a result of trying to solve a problem. Have you ever invented anything? If so, write about your invention in the space below.

____

____

____

Create an Acrostic

Poetry is a creative and imaginative way of using words to communicate ideas, feelings, and concepts to the reader. The reader must often use his or her imagination as the words are read.

An **acrostic** is a special kind of poem. The name of a person, place, or thing is written in a vertical (up-and-down) line. In other words, the first letters of the lines spell the name of the subject of the poem. You may use the first name, the last name, or both. The lines do not have to rhyme.

A sample acrostic follows:

EDISON

Electricity we use was his gift to us.
Didn't give up when things went wrong.
Inventive genius.
Stock ticker tape machine was his idea.
Over 1,000 patents.
Nicknamed the Wizard of Menlo Park.

Create an original acrostic poem about a well-known creative person. Write your rough draft in the space below. Then rewrite your final poem on another sheet of paper.

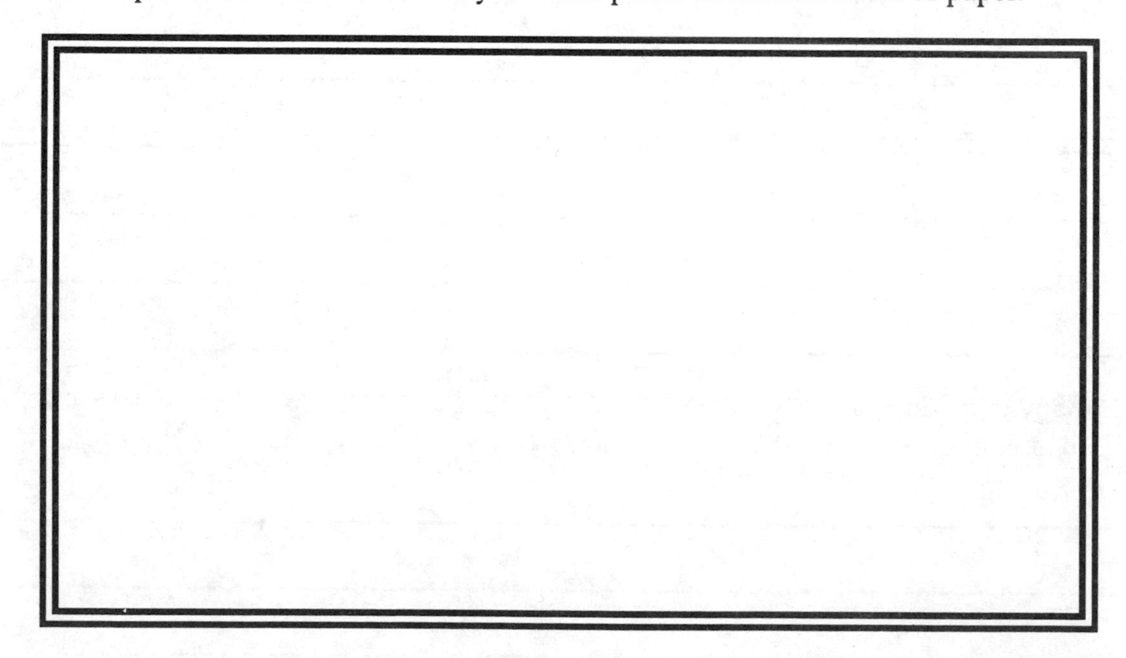

Thomas Edison

Thomas Edison was a prolific inventor. In fact, he was granted 1,076 patents—more than any other person. He said that he was interested in inventing things that would make people's lives easier, were easy to use, and easy to fix. Among his greatest inventions were the electric light bulb, motion pictures, the phonograph, the stock ticker tape machine, an improved telephone, and the mimeograph machine. The period of history when Edison was producing so many wondrous things is often called The Age of Edison.

Some people believe that Thomas Edison was the greatest inventor ever to live. Read a biography of Thomas Edison. Prepare an essay explaining why you do or do not agree that he was the greatest inventor of all time. Use the form below to help you get started.

TITLE AND AUTHOR:________________________________

List at least ten facts that you learned about Thomas Edison from reading the biography.

1. ________________________________
2. ________________________________
3. ________________________________
4. ________________________________
5. ________________________
6. ________________________
7. ________________________
8. ________________________
9. ________________________
10. ________________________________

What else might you want to learn before coming to your conclusion?

____

____

____

Write your report on another sheet of paper.

Creative People Bibliography

Create a bibliography of biographies of creative people. Include at least six books, using the correct form. An example follows:

Hogrogian, Robert. *George Washington Carver.* Hawthorne, NJ: January Productions, Inc., 1981.

———. *Thomas Alva Edison.* Hawthorne, NJ: January Productions, Inc., 1981.

The books are listed alphabetically by the author's last name. If two lines are needed for an entry, the second line is indented. Titles of books are in italics. If you do not have italic type or if you are writing by hand, then you underline the title. Note that a long dash is used when more than one book is written by the same author. Also note the proper punctuation throughout the entry.

CREATIVE PEOPLE BIBLIOGRAPHY

Read one of the books on your list. (Do not choose the same book as for the Thomas Edison activity.) Write a paragraph explaining why you did or did not like this book.

____

____

____

____

____

____

____

Seeing Things Differently

Creative people often have the ability to see things in new and unusual ways. For example, many inventions were created because the inventor was able to see new ways of doing things and/or new uses for existing objects.

An artist who was able to see things in ways different from the way the rest of us see things was Spanish artist Pablo Picasso, who lived from 1881–1973. Along with French artist Georges Braque, Picasso is credited with founding the style of abstract painting known as **cubism**.

Research Pablo Picasso and the art form he cofounded.

Pretend that you are a guide in an art museum. You have been asked to explain cubism to a group of students visiting the museum on a field trip. Prepare a speech in which you will give an explanation of what cubism is and the impact it had on Picasso and the rest of the art world. Try to find examples of his work in this style to share with the group. Use the form below to help you prepare your talk. Write your presentation on another sheet of paper.

Facts about Pablo Picasso:

____

____

____

____

Facts about cubism:

____

____

____

Impact of cubism and Picasso on the rest of the art world:

____

____

Examples of Picasso's work in this style:

____

____

____

Create a Jingle

People who invent things are creative. Once their products become a reality, however, they often require the services of other creative people to advertise the products! Often the ads they create include a musical advertising slogan, called a jingle.

Choose one of the products listed below. Pretend that it was just invented and that you have been asked to create a musical ad for it. Before you begin, see if you can find out some interesting facts about the invention.

safety pin	**velcro**	**sewing machine**	**leaf blower**
telephone	**automobile**	**instant coffee**	**microwave oven**
personal pager	**microwave oven**	**magic markers**	**zipper**

INVENTION: ______________________________

WHAT MAKES THIS PRODUCT DIFFERENT:

____

____

____

____

____

Are you going to create an original tune or are you going to adapt an existing tune? If you have decided to adapt an existing tune, name that tune.

____

Create your jingle in the space below.

____

____

____

____

____

____

Section IV:

Natural Wonders

Such Wonders!

The term "natural wonder" usually refers to an area that is an example of extraordinary natural beauty, oddity, extremity, grandeur, and/or rarity. Natural wonders exist in many places around the world. They include geysers, islands, volcanoes, waterfalls, monoliths, fjords, and reefs.

Some of the world's natural wonders are listed below.

Acadia National Park, Maine
Angel Falls, Venezuela
Arches National Park, Utah
Ayers Rock, Australia
Benbulben, Ireland
Big Sur, California
Bora Bora, French Polynesia
Bryce Canyon, Utah
Cape Horn, Chile
Carlsbad Cavern, New Mexico
Cathedral Grove, British Columbia, Canada
Chimney Rock, Nebraska
Cliffs of Etretat, France
Colombia Icefield, British Columbia, Canada
Cotopaxi, Ecuador
Crater Lake, Oregon
Craters of the Moon, Idaho
Dades Gorges, Morocco
Dead Sea, Israel/Jordan
Death Valley, California
Dettifloss, Iceland
Devil's Tower, Washington
Dolomite Mountains, Italy
El Capitan, California
Everglades National Park, Florida
Fingal's Cave, Scotland
Geiranger Fjord, Norway
Giant's Causeway, Ireland
Grand Canyon , Arizona
Grand Teton National Park, Wyoming
Great Barrier Reef, Australia
Hienghene Bay, New Caledonia
Holloch Cave, Switzerland
Hudson River, New York/New Jersey
Hunlen Falls, British Columbia, Canada
Iguassu Falls, British Columbia, Canada
Mammoth Hot Springs, Wyoming
Mt. Olga, Australia
Mt. McKinley, Alaska
Old Faithful, Wyoming
Old Man of Hoy, Scotland
Painted Desert, Arizona
Petrified Forest, Arizona
Rock of Gibraltar, Spain
Simpson Desert, Australia
Surtsey, Iceland
Stone Mountain, Georgia
The Badlands, South Dakota
Victoria Falls, Zimbabwe
Yellowstone National Park, Wyoming
Yosemite National Park, California
Zion National Park, Utah

Choose three, each from a different continent. List those natural wonders below. After conducting research, write a well-constructed, one- or two-paragraph summary for each of the three. Use other paper. Perhaps you can find a photograph, picture post card, or magazine article to add to your summary. Share your findings with your class.

NATURAL WONDER **LOCATION**

1.

2.

3.

Where in the World?

For each term listed below, write a definition and tell where in the world an example can be found. Be sure to use complete sentences.

1. **butte:**
2. **cataract:**
3. **fjord:**
4. **geyser:**
5. **glacier:**
6. **hot spring:**
7. **monolith:**
8. **waterfall:**

Choose one of the geographical features from the first part of this activity. Write two or more paragraphs describing the geography of the region in which an example of this feature can be found.

The Power of Nature

Many natural wonders were formed as a result of the tremendous physical forces of nature. Volcanic eruptions, earthquakes, and the movement of glaciers and rivers are examples of these forces. For example, some mountains are formed by earthquakes. When the plates of the earth's surface move toward each other, they are pushed together, forming "wrinkles" in the earth's crust.

Write three paragraphs in which you give the scientific explanation of each of the following natural wonders: geyser, fjord (fiord), and coral reef.

Natural Wonder Habitat

A **habitat** is defined as the environment where a plant or animal naturally lives. There are many different types of habitats: tundra, woodland forest, rain forest, desert, wetland, swamp, marsh, seaside (tidal pool), ocean, fresh water (lake, river), mountain, and prairie.

Choose a natural wonder and research that natural wonder. Write a short essay that describes the natural wonder as a habitat. Describe the animals and plants that live in the habitat. Also explain one of the food chains that exists in the habitat. Include a diagram of the food chain.

Use this form to help you organize your writing. Write your essay on other paper.

NATURAL WONDER: ______________________________

LOCATION: ______________________________

TYPE OF HABITAT: ______________________________

WILDLIFE FOUND THERE: ______________________________

____

____

____

PLANT LIFE FOUND THERE: ______________________________

____

____

____

____

ONE FOOD CHAIN THAT EXISTS THERE: ______________________________

____

____

____

____

____

____

____

Measurement Word Problems

You are often asked to **solve** math word problems. In this exercise, you are asked to **write** one! Be sure the information you use is accurate!

Below is an example of a word problem based on facts about natural wonders:

Angel Falls of the Guiana Highlands in South America is a waterfall 3,212 feet high. This is quite a spectacular sight. It is the highest waterfall in the world! This is almost twenty times the plunge of Niagara Falls. Based on that information, determine the approximate height of Niagara Falls.

SOLUTION:

3,212 feet ÷ 20 =160

Niagara Falls is about a 160-foot plunge.

Write a measurement word problem based on facts about one or more natural wonders. Be sure that those facts are accurate. Double check your work to make sure that you know the correct solution. Write your problem in the space provided. Exchange with classmates to solve.

WORD PROBLEM:

What a Trip! Can We Afford It?

Many wonderful sightseeing tours of the natural wonders of the American West are available.

An 8-day (7-night) trip offered by one tour company takes participants to the following places: the Grand Canyon, Zion National Park, Oak Creek Canyon, and Bryce National Park. Using the following facts about this tour, create two math word problems.

Included are 7 breakfasts, 5 lunches, and 7 dinners.

The cost is $1,490.00 per person for each of two people.

The cost for a third person staying in the same room is $1,399.

A husband, wife, and their twelve-year-old daughter want to take the trip.

An optional 4-hour flight over Monument Valley Tribal Park costs $120.00 per person.

Two optional boxed lunches may be purchased at $10.00 per person.

Write two word problems based on the above information. You do not have to use all the facts in your problems and you may add other facts. Make sure that you know the correct solutions to your problems. Exchange problems with your classmates. Compare your solutions.

WORD PROBLEM #1:

____

____

____

SOLUTION:

WORD PROBLEM #2:

____

____

____

SOLUTION:

Protecting Our Natural Wonders

Many natural wonders contain potentially valuable resources. The rain forests of Brazil and Venezuela, for example, have minerals, lumber, and rich soil for farming. These forests are being depleted in order to obtain the resources. Thousands of plant and animal species have become extinct or endangered as a result.

Choose a natural wonder that you think should be protected by law from development and/or the harvesting of resources. Prepare a written persuasive argument presenting your point of view. Remember, to be persuasive you must use logic as well as emotion. Try to have some facts to back up your sentiments. Use the space below to write your first draft. Check your work and then rewrite your argument on another sheet of paper.

NATURAL WONDER TO BE PROTECTED: ______________________

LOCATION: ______________________

REASON FOR PROTECTING IT BY LAW:

Figurative Language

Figurative language helps readers create mental pictures that make reading a description more interesting and vivid. The following are three types of figurative language:

Metaphor: A metaphor is a comparison between two unlike things without the use of "like" or "as."

EXAMPLE: The forest floor was a green carpet.

Simile: A simile is a comparison between two unlike things with the use of "like" or "as."

EXAMPLE: The memory was like a knife cutting into him.

Personification: Personification is the bestowing of human characteristics on lifeless objects or abstract ideas.

EXAMPLE: The day caught up with him and he slept.

Locate photographs and/or descriptions of each natural wonder listed below. Add one or two of your own. Think of several examples of figurative language to describe each. Try to use all three forms of figurative language. Be creative and have fun!

NATURAL WONDER	DESCRIPTION USING FIGURATIVE LANGUAGE
El Capitan	____________________
	____________________
The Rock of Gibraltar	____________________
	____________________
Mt. McKinley	____________________
	____________________
Ayers Rock	____________________
	____________________
Mt. Etna	____________________
	____________________
Victoria Falls	____________________
	____________________
Other	____________________
	____________________

Create a Poem

Poetry is a special form of writing. It creatively and imaginatively transfers an idea from the poet to the reader. The poet may use words as symbols, alliteration, figurative language, and very descriptive phrases. Poetry is composed—much like music is composed—with attention to rhythm and/or rhyme. Some poetry has a formal structure based on the number of syllables. Examples are the sonnet, the haiku, and the cinquain. Other poems are unstructured; we call this free verse. Regardless of whether or not it begins a new sentence, each line in a poem is usually capitalized.

Below is an example of a poem about a natural wonder. It is called "The Painted Desert." The Painted Desert, located in Arizona, is renowned for its beautiful colors.

The Painted Desert

Red, yellow, gold and purple it sings.
The dryness is quiet, yet it brings
A pink whisper of peace and solitude.
The colorful quiet, a rainbow of peace.
I thirst for its indigo shadows of rest,
I drink in the turquoise tranquility,
And I am quenched by the glow of amber sand.

Choose a natural wonder from the activity entitled Such Wonders! Write a poem describing the wonder or expressing your feelings about it. Before you begin to write your poem, you should research the location. Make notes about it that you will incorporate in your poem. Then write your poem on another sheet of paper. Illustrate your poem.

NATURAL WONDER:______________________________

INTERESTING FACTS ABOUT THE NATURAL WONDER:

____

____

____

____

____

____

____

____

How Can You Explain It?

People living near a natural wonder often created a myth or legend to explain its existence or purpose. Legend tells us, for example, that the Grand Canyon was formed by the mythical hero Paul Bunyan, a giant lumberjack. Read the legend of Paul Bunyan. Write a paragraph summarizing how Paul Bunyan caused the formation of the Grand Canyon.

Now choose another natural wonder. Some possibilities are Devil's Tower, Wyoming; Arches National Park, Utah; Stone Mountain, Georgia; Big Sur, California; Old Man of Hoy, Scotland; The Dead Sea, Israel; and the Simpson Desert, Australia. Research the natural wonder. Then write an original myth or legend about it. Use the form below to help you get started. Write your story on another sheet of paper. Read your story to the class at a designated time. Your teacher may wish to assemble the myths and legends into a class book.

NATURAL WONDER: ____________________

LOCATION: ____________________

HOW IT WAS CREATED IN REALITY: ____________________

HOW IT WAS CREATED ACCORDING TO MY MYTH: ____________________

What's the Setting?

With your teacher's approval, choose a short story or popular children's novel that has a natural wonder as its setting. An example is *Brighty of Grand Canyon,* by Marguerite Henry. Brainstorm with your class to name some others. You might also like to ask your librarian or media specialist for help in adding to the list you create.

1. *Brighty of Grand Canyon*
2.
3.
4.
5.
6.
7.
8.
9.
10.

After you have read the short story or novel, complete the following form.

TITLE OF BOOK OR STORE: ______________________________

AUTHOR: ______________________________

MAIN THEME: ______________________________

____

SUMMARY OF THE PLOT: ______________________________

____

____

____

____

____

HOW THE SETTING WAS IMPORTANT TO THE STORY: ______________________________

____

____

____

____

____

Nature in Art

The natural wonders of the world have encouraged many artists to try to capture their images, sometimes at great risk. Museums have many examples of this type of art. Perhaps you were lucky enough to see some!

America has been blessed with many fine examples of natural wonders. Using the resources of the library, an encyclopedia, and/or the internet, locate an example of a work of art that is based on a natural wonder of the United States. Write one to three paragraphs about the natural wonder. Explain how the artist chose the subject and any interesting facts you have learned concerning the completion of the work.

Complete the chart below to help you get started. Try to locate a reproduction, post card, or poster of the work of art to accompany your writing.

TITLE OF WORK OF ART: ______________________________

ARTIST: ______________________________

SUBJECT: ______________________________

____

____

____

INTERESTING FACTS ABOUT COMPLETION OF THE WORK: ______________

____

____

____

____

____

____

____

____

____

____

Create a Song

Write an original song to sing the praises of a natural wonder. Begin by thinking of the melody of a well-known song. Create original lyrics to accompany the tune. For example, you might choose the tune of "Oh, Susanna!" and substitute the words "Oh, Grand Canyon!"

Write the lyrics for at least five lines. Record your original song and play it for your classmates. If possible, distribute copies of the lyrics to your classmates so that they can sing along with you. Have fun!

Complete the chart below to help you get started.

THE NATURAL WONDER: ______________________________

THE POPULAR SONG USED: ______________________________

PHYSICAL DESCRIPTION OF THE WONDER: ______________________________

____

____

____

____

WRITE YOUR SONG IN THE SPACE BELOW.

____

____

____

____

____

____

____

____

____

____

____

Optional Writing Activities

ANCIENT CIVILIZATIONS

1. Research the original Olympics held in ancient Greece. Make a list of the events that were held at that time. Pretend you are a sportscaster at one of the athletic contests. Describe the action in a well-written story. Present it to your class orally in the form of a sportscast.
2. Research the great pharaohs of ancient Egypt. Sesostris III, Thutmose III, Tutankhamen and Ramses II are some famous ones. Investigate and evaluate their powers and lifestyles. With a group of students, write short skits about the pharaohs and present them to the class. Use costumes and props.
3. Investigate foods of ancient Greece and Rome. How was food prepared? Which foods were popular? Compare and contrast the foods of these ancient civilizations with those of modern ones. Create an ancient Greek and Roman recipe book. Prepare one dish to share with your classmates.

THE SEA

1. Read Jules Verne's exciting fantasy sea adventure, *Twenty Thousand Leagues Under the Sea.* Prepare a book report describing the highlights of the story. Present it orally to your classmates.
2. Report on oceanography, the science of the sea. Learn how scientists study and explore the ocean bottom. What types of technology are now used? How do sound echoes give us information? Forecast future uses of the sea. Place your written information and pictures on a classroom bulletin board display.
3. Because of shipwrecks, oceans are sometimes the sites of great hoards of treasure and information about the past. Just think of the *Titanic!* Research information about famous shipwrecks. Create a roller movie about one. Write a script to accompany your movie.

CREATIVE PEOPLE

1. Choose an invention. Explain why it is an important part of your life.
2. Write a paragraph about a not-so-well-known person you consider to be creative. Explain why you think he or she is creative.
3. Answer the following questions in two or three well-crafted paragraphs: Do you consider yourself to be a creative person? If yes, in what ways? If not, why not? What might help you to become more creative? Are there disadvantages to being a creative person?

NATURAL WONDERS

1. Write a letter to a government leader explaining what you would like done to protect a particular natural wonder.
2. Learn about John Muir and Theodore Roosevelt. Evaluate their influence on the natural wonders of America. Write a paragraph explaining your opinion.
3. If you could visit any natural wonder of the world, which would you choose? Write a paragraph in which you state the reasons for that choice.

Bibliography

ANCIENT CIVILIZATIONS

Evslin, Bernard. *Heroes, Gods, and Monsters of the Greek Myths.* New York: Bantam Books, 1975.

Forman, Joan. *The Romans.* Morristown, NJ: Silver Burdett Co., 1985.

Jones, John E. *Ancient Greece.* Morristown, NJ: Silver Burdett Co., 1985.

Millard, Ann. *Egypt.* New York: Franklin Watts Co., 1985.

Snyder, Zilpha. *The Egypt Game.* New York: Dell Publishing, 1967.

Stark, Rebecca. *Archaeology.* Hawthorne, NJ: Educational Impressions, 1994.

———. *Mythology.* Hawthorne, NJ: Educational Impressions, 1994.

THE SEA

Buck, Pearl S. *The Big Wave* New York: Harper Collins, 1976.

Pick, Christopher. *Under Sea.* London: Usbourne Co., 1982.

Sperry, Armstrong. *Call It Courage.* New York: Macmillan Co., 1968.

CREATIVE PEOPLE

Benjamin, Alan. *One Thousand Inventions.* New York: Scholastic Books, 1980.

Finkbinder, Marion; Sue Jeweler; Jim McAlpine; and Betty Weincek. *Creative Problem Solving: Faces of Man, The Arts.* Hawthorne, NJ: Educational Impressions, Inc., 1989.

———. *Creative Problem Solving: Faces of Man, The Sciences.* Hawthorne, NJ: Educational Impressions, Inc., 1989.

Kane, Nathan. *Famous First Facts, Fourth Edition.* New York: The H.W. Wilson Company, 1981.

COMMISSIONER OF PATENTS: U.S. Patent & Trademark Office, Washington, D.C. 20231

NATURAL WONDERS

Butler, Daphne. *What Happens When Volcanoes Erupt?* Chatham, NJ: Steck-Vaughn, 1995.

Cox, Reg and Neil Morris. *The Seven Wonders of the Natural World.* Parsippany, NJ: Silver Burdett Press, 1996.

Jordan, Martin and Tanis Jordan. *Angel Falls, A South American Journey*. New York: Kingfisher Chambers, Inc., 1995.

Natural Wonders of the World. Pleasantville, NY: Readers Digest Association, 1980.

INTERNET LISTINGS

www.Yahooligans.com (Ancient Egypt, Greece, and Rome)

ww.Nationalgeographic.com/kids (Oceans of the World)

http://pharos.bu.edu/Egypt/Wonders/pyramid.html (Ancient Egypt)

http://www.book.vci.edu/Books/moon/volcanoes. Html (Hawaii's Volcanoes)

http://www/nps.gov/yell (Yellowstone National Park)

http://www.flagstaff.az.us/meteor (Meteor Crater)